TIPS

1. Explain that scissors are useful but need to be used carefully.
2. Always use children's scissors with them.
3. If your child is left handed, be sure to purchase left handed scissors.

WHY ARE SCISSOR SKILLS SO IMPORTANT?

With the opening and closing motion of cutting, it allows children to develop the small muscles in their hands. These muscles are so important for writing or doing everyday things.

Develop Hand-eye coordination what is important for catching balls, eating with a spoon.

Using scissors takes concentration and attention to detail which will be used in all aspects of your childs's future life.

INSTRUCTION

STEP 1.
Cut out the sheet if you want

STEP 2.
Color the picture if possible

STEP 3.
Carefully cut out the picture or elements

STEP 4.
Paste! Have FUN!

1.
2.
3.
4.
cut
glue
color

1.
2.
3.
4.
cut
glue
color

1.
2.
3.
4.
cut
glue
color

Cut and Paste. What Comes Next?

Cut and Paste. What Comes Next?

 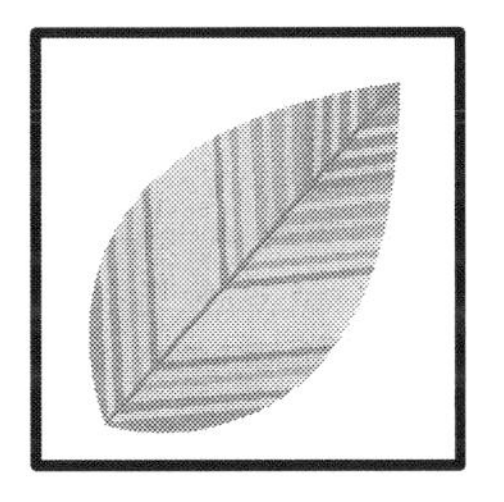 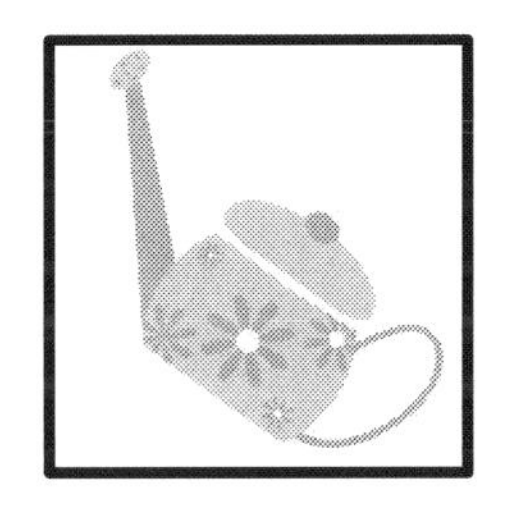  

  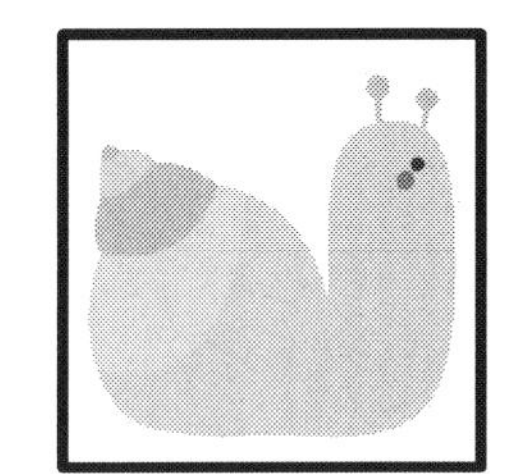  

Cut and Paste. What Comes Next?

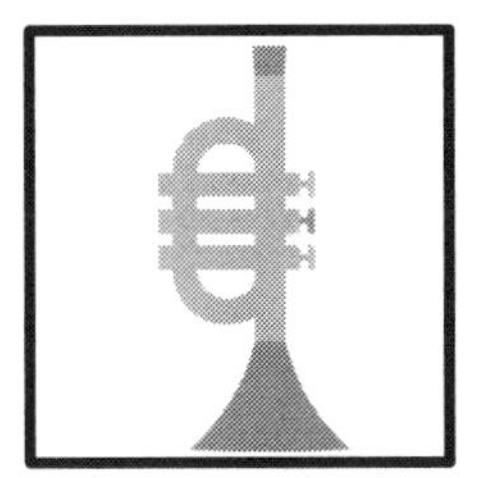

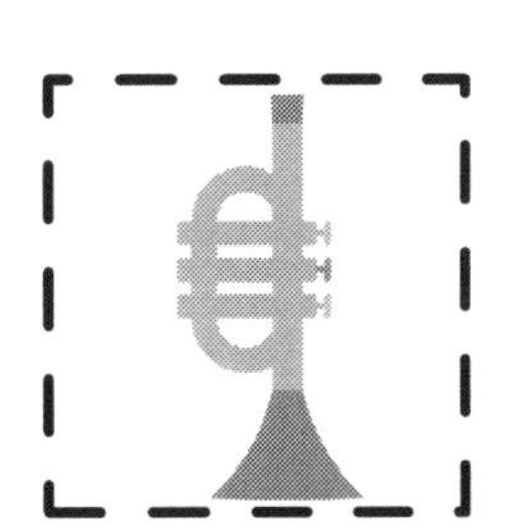

color
cut
glue

Paste here!

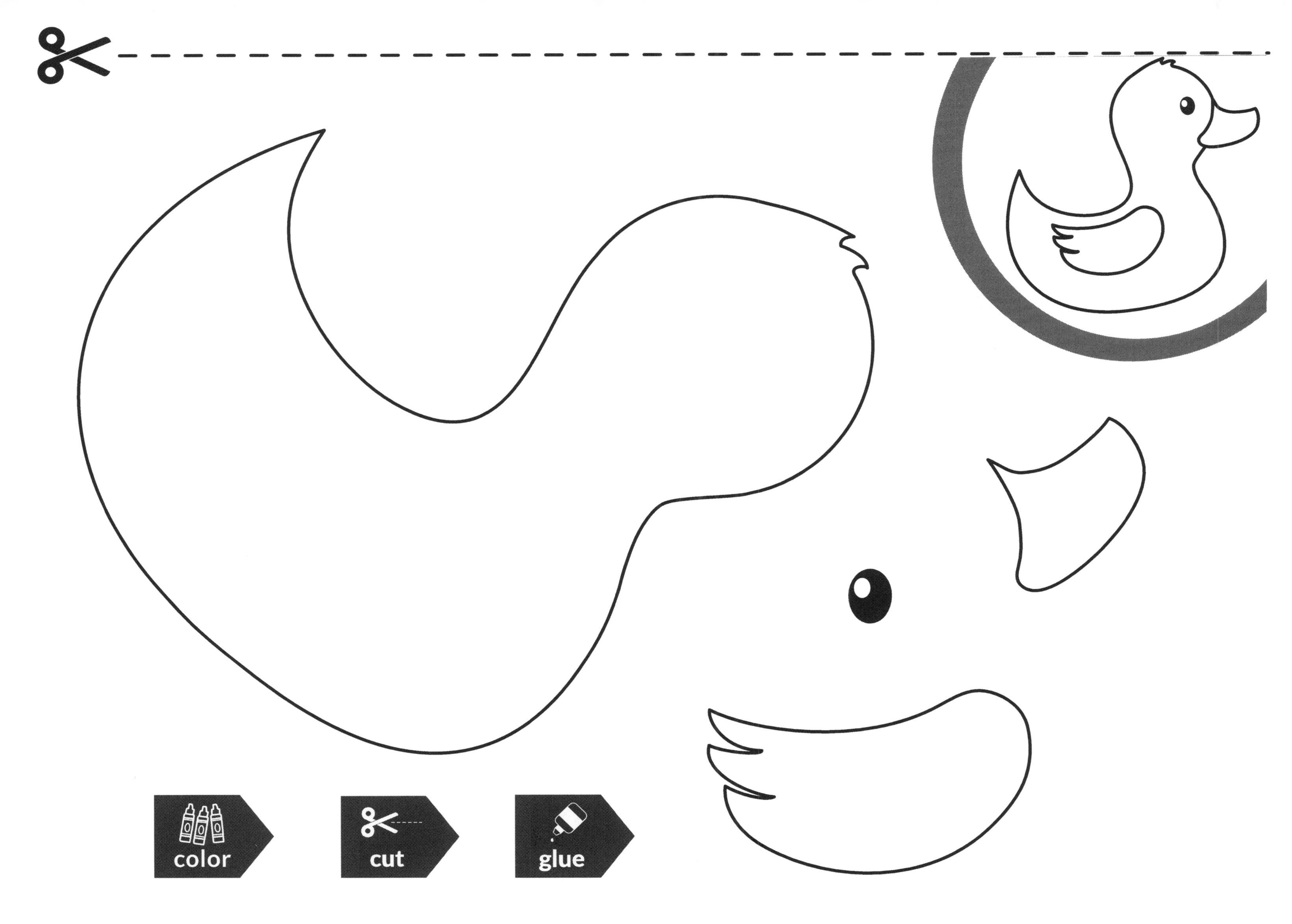
color
cut
glue

Paste here!

color
cut
glue

Paste here!

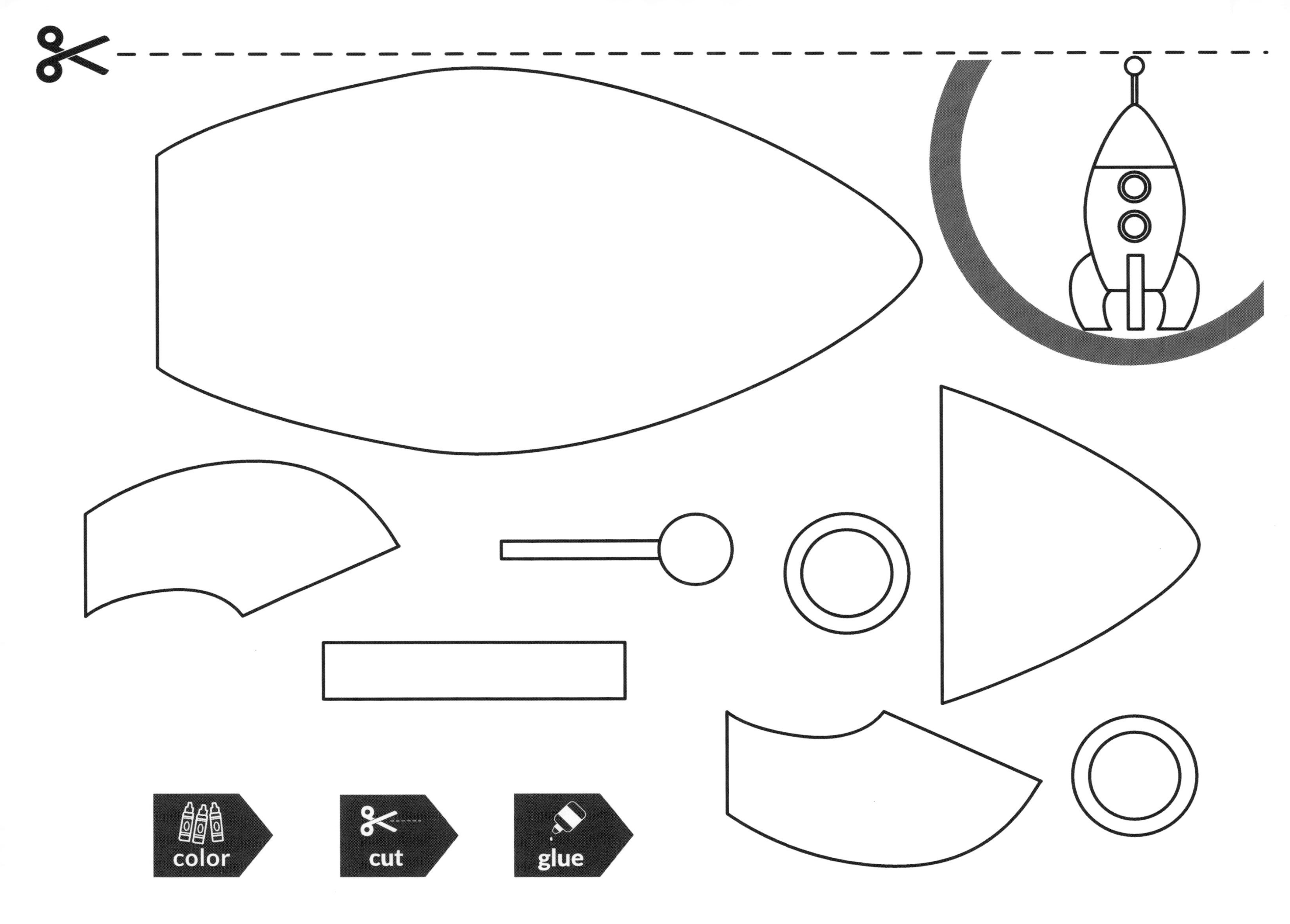
color
cut
glue

Paste here!

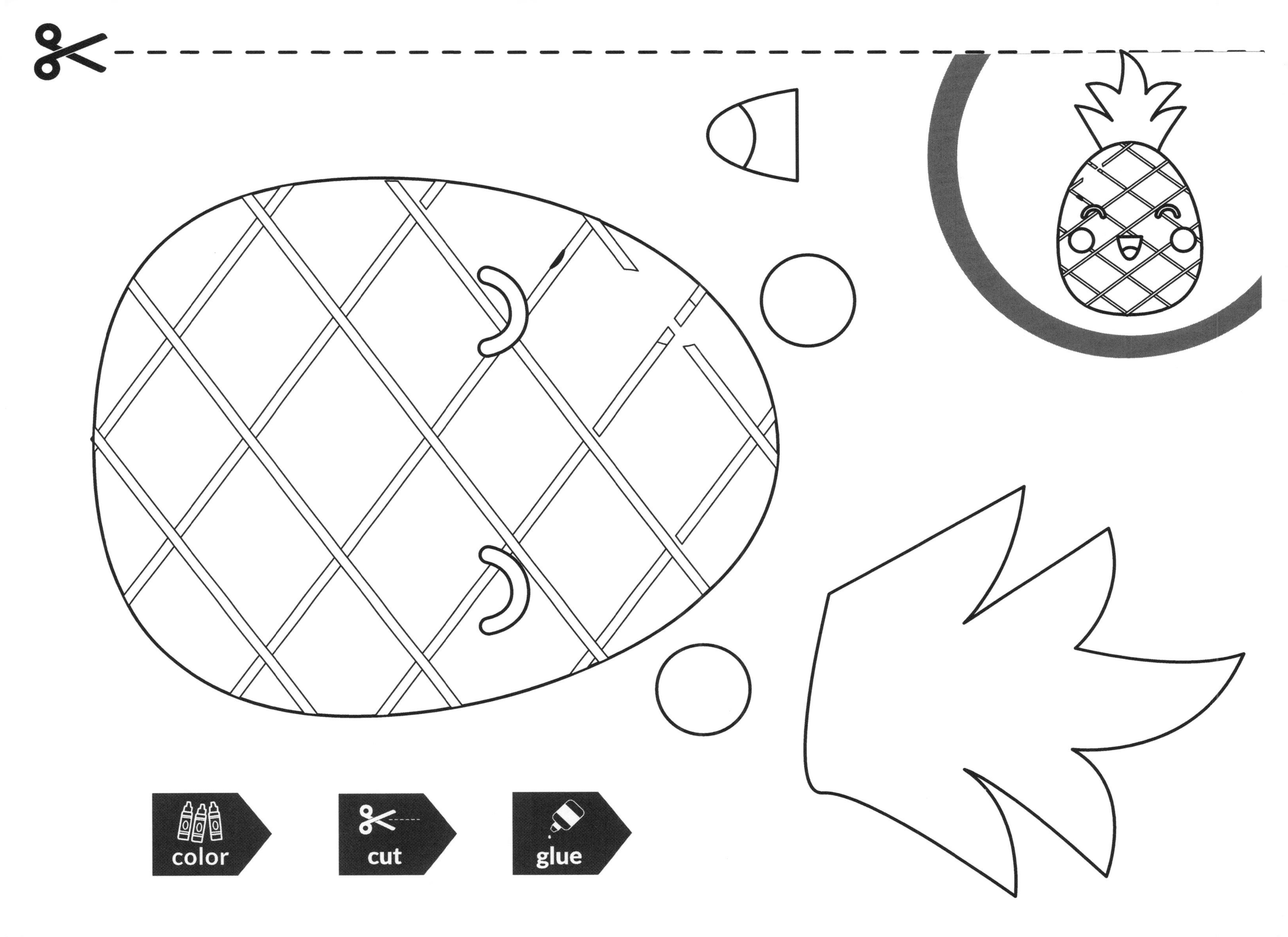
color
cut
glue

Paste here!

Cut the Puzzles and paste them on the next page

Paste here!

Cut the Puzzles and paste them on the next page

Paste here!

Cut the Puzzles and paste them on the next page

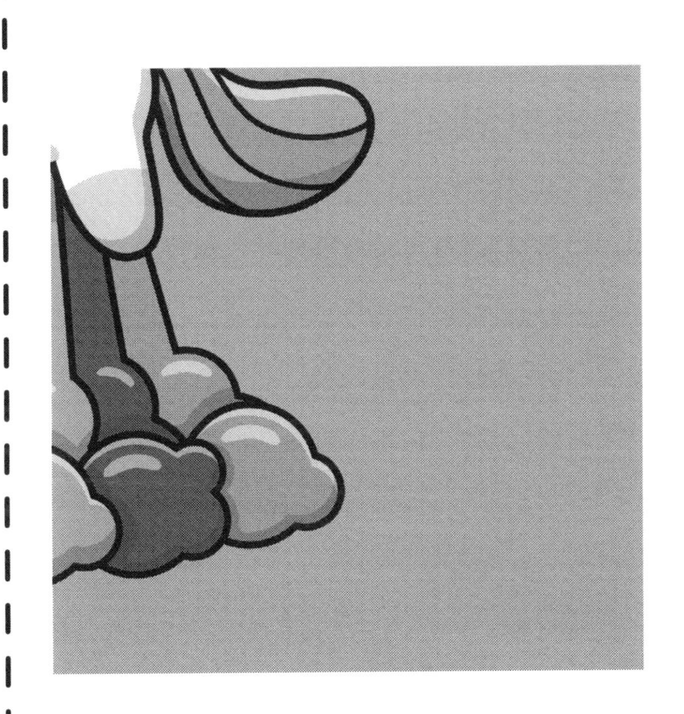

Paste here!

Cut the Puzzles and paste them on the next page

Paste here!

Cut the Puzzles and paste them on the next page

Paste here!

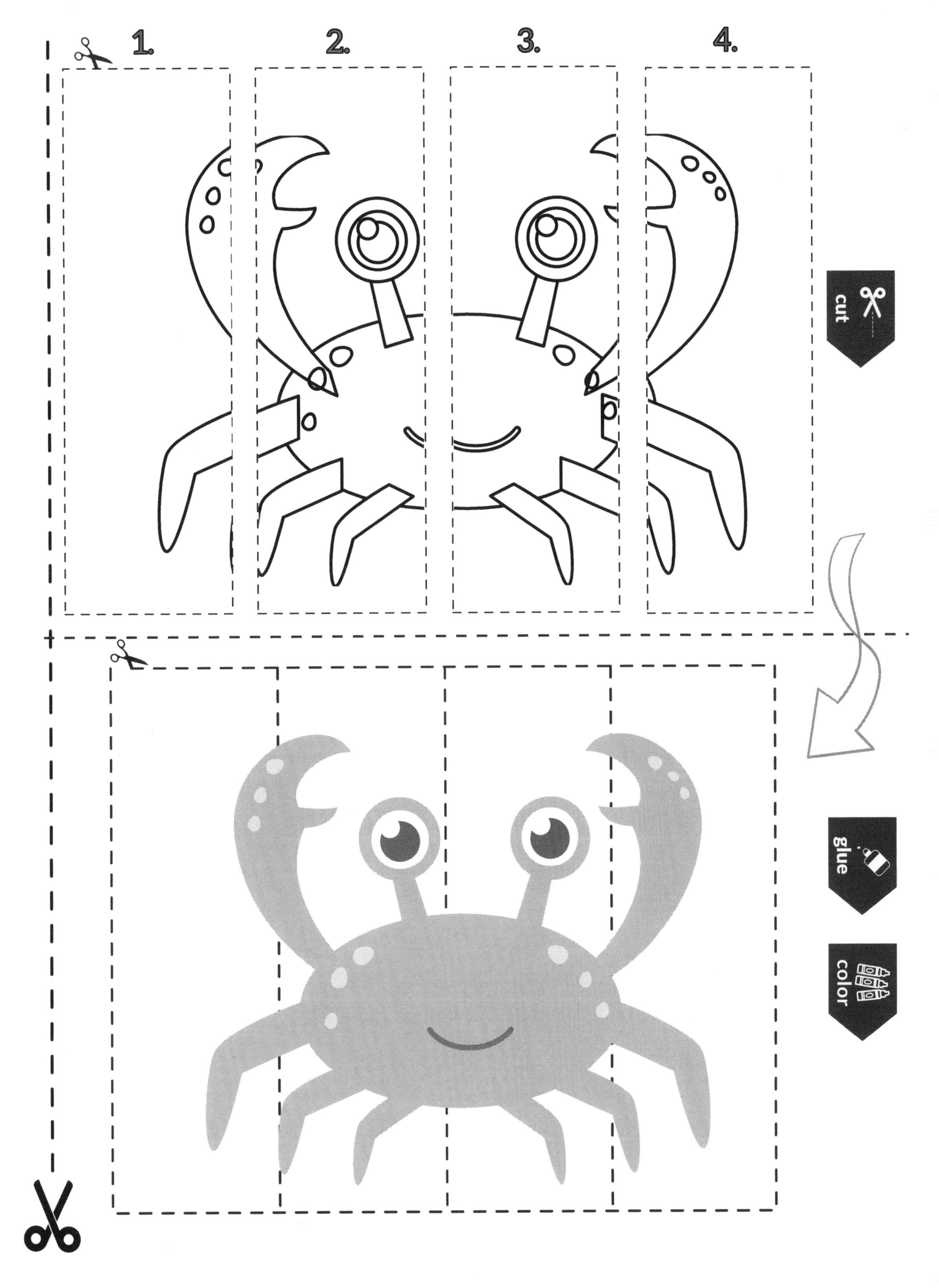
1.
2.
3.
4.
cut
glue
color

1.
2.
3.
4.
cut
glue
color

Cut and Paste. What Comes Next?

Cut and Paste. What Comes Next?

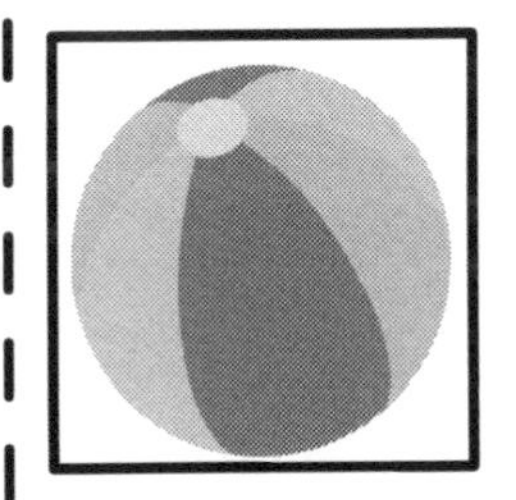  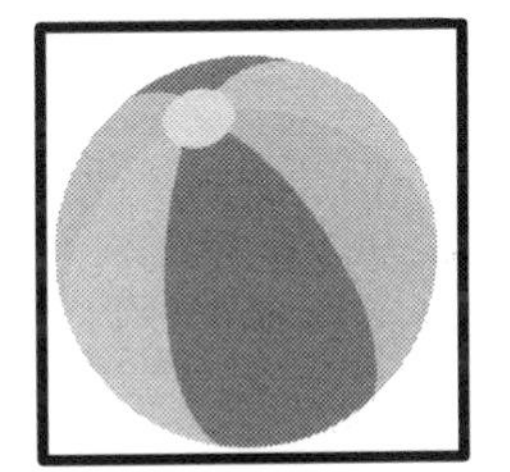  

   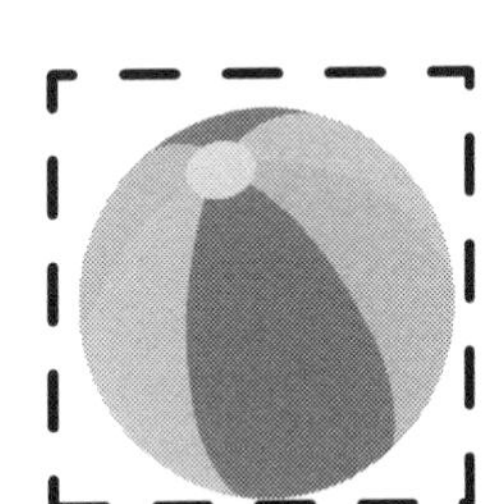

color
cut
glue

Paste here!

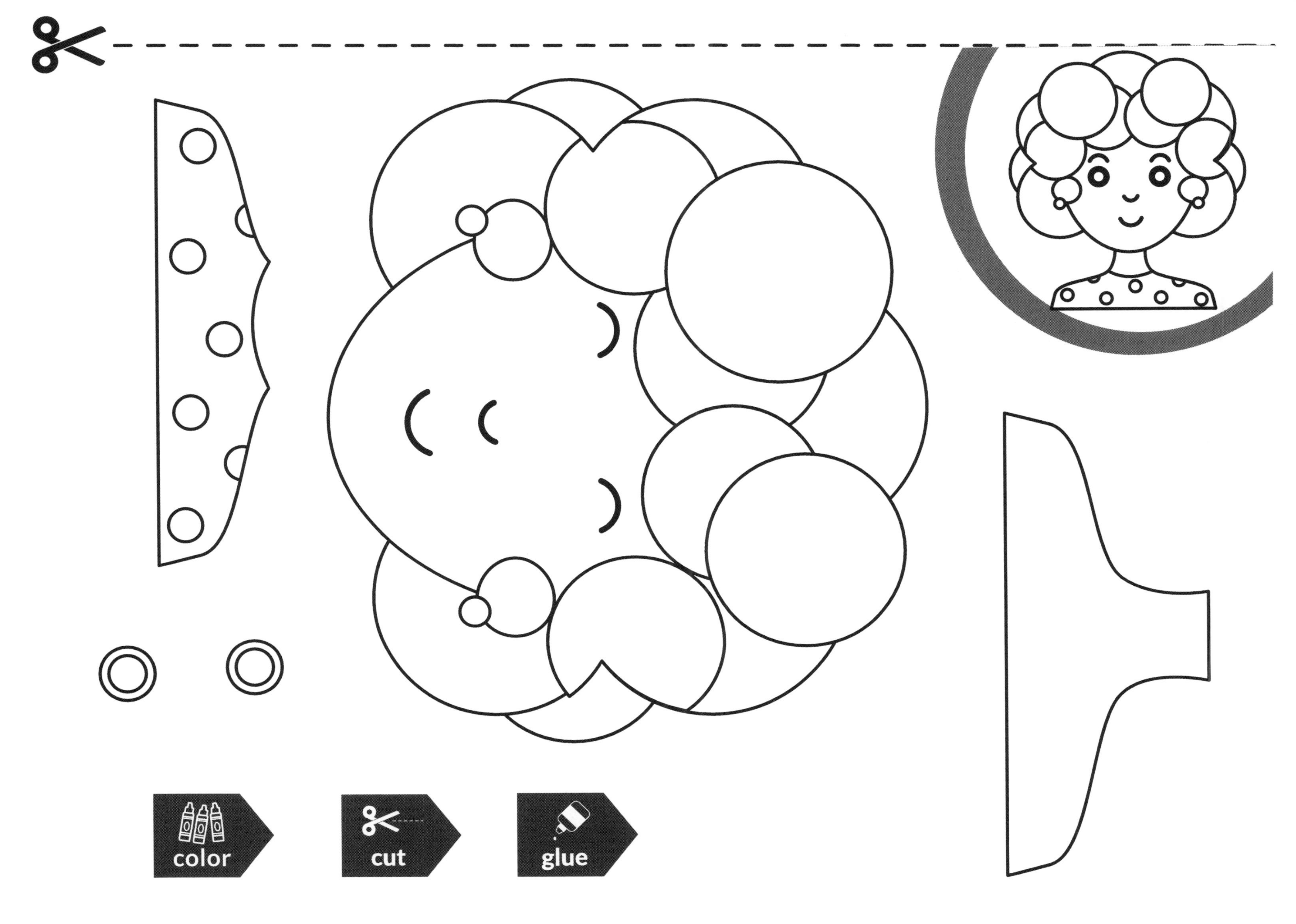
color
cut
glue

Paste here!

color
cut
glue

Paste here!

color
cut
glue

Paste here!

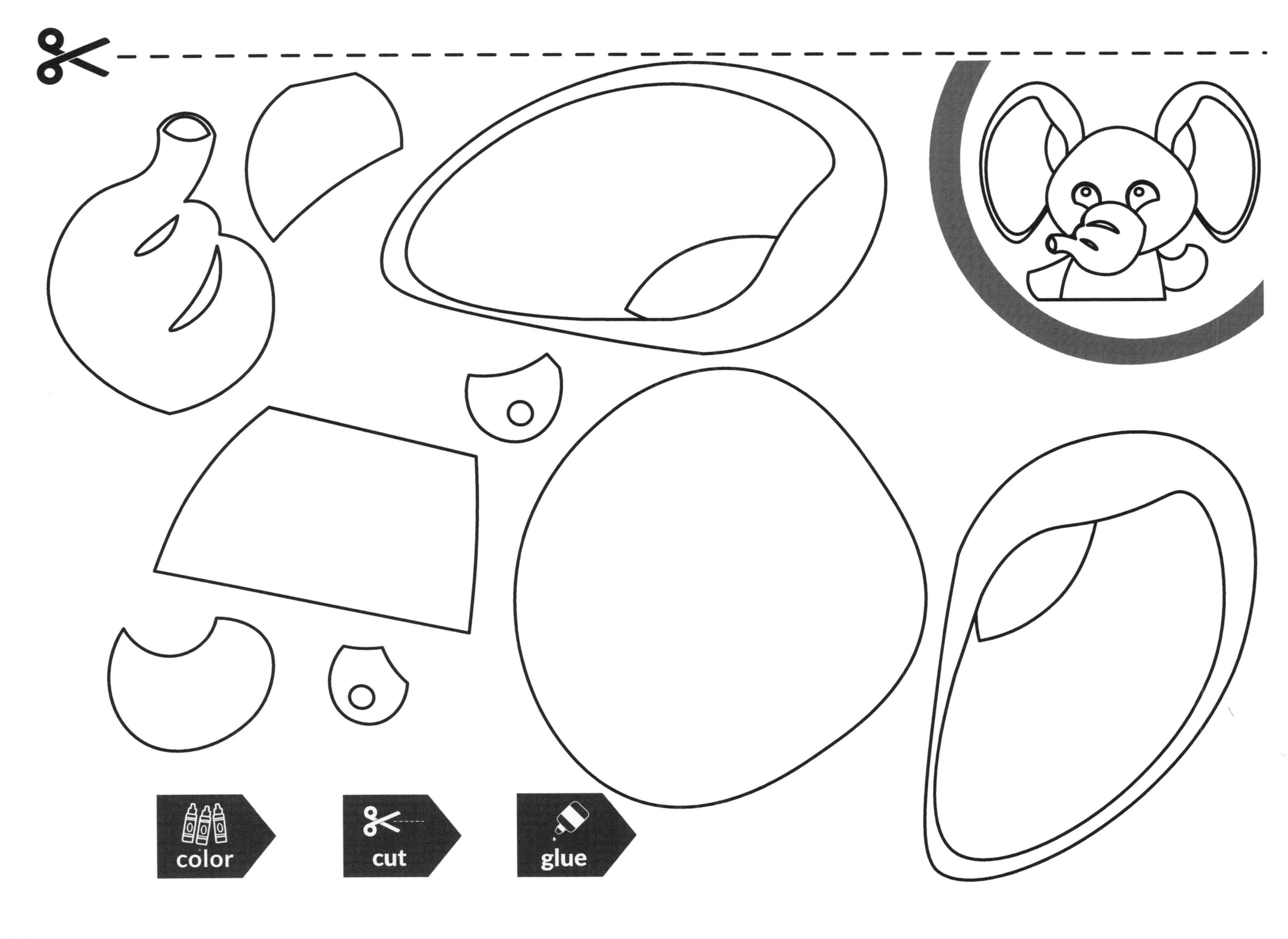
color
cut
glue

Paste here!

Find match and paste the pictures together

Find match and paste the pictures together

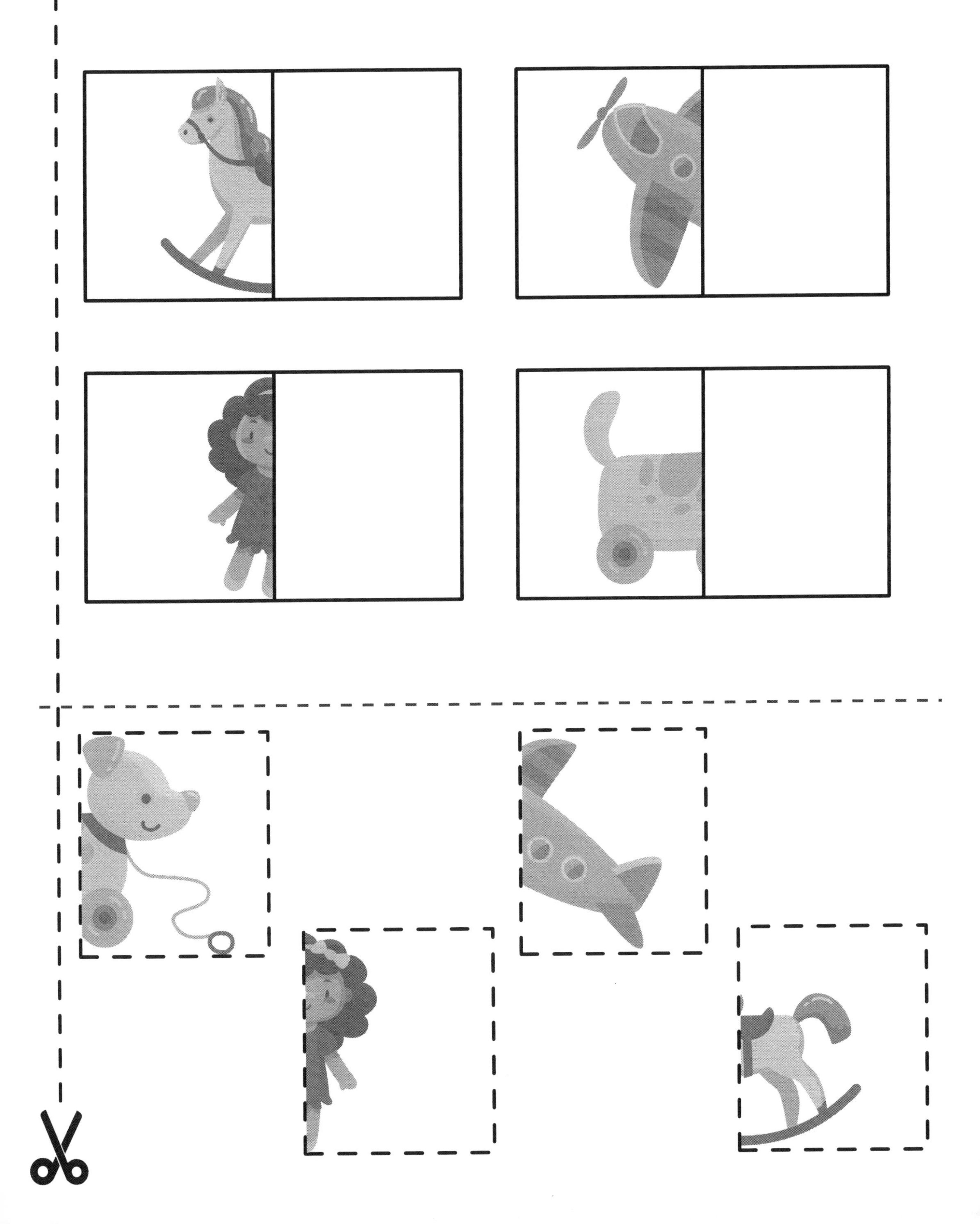

Find match and paste the pictures together

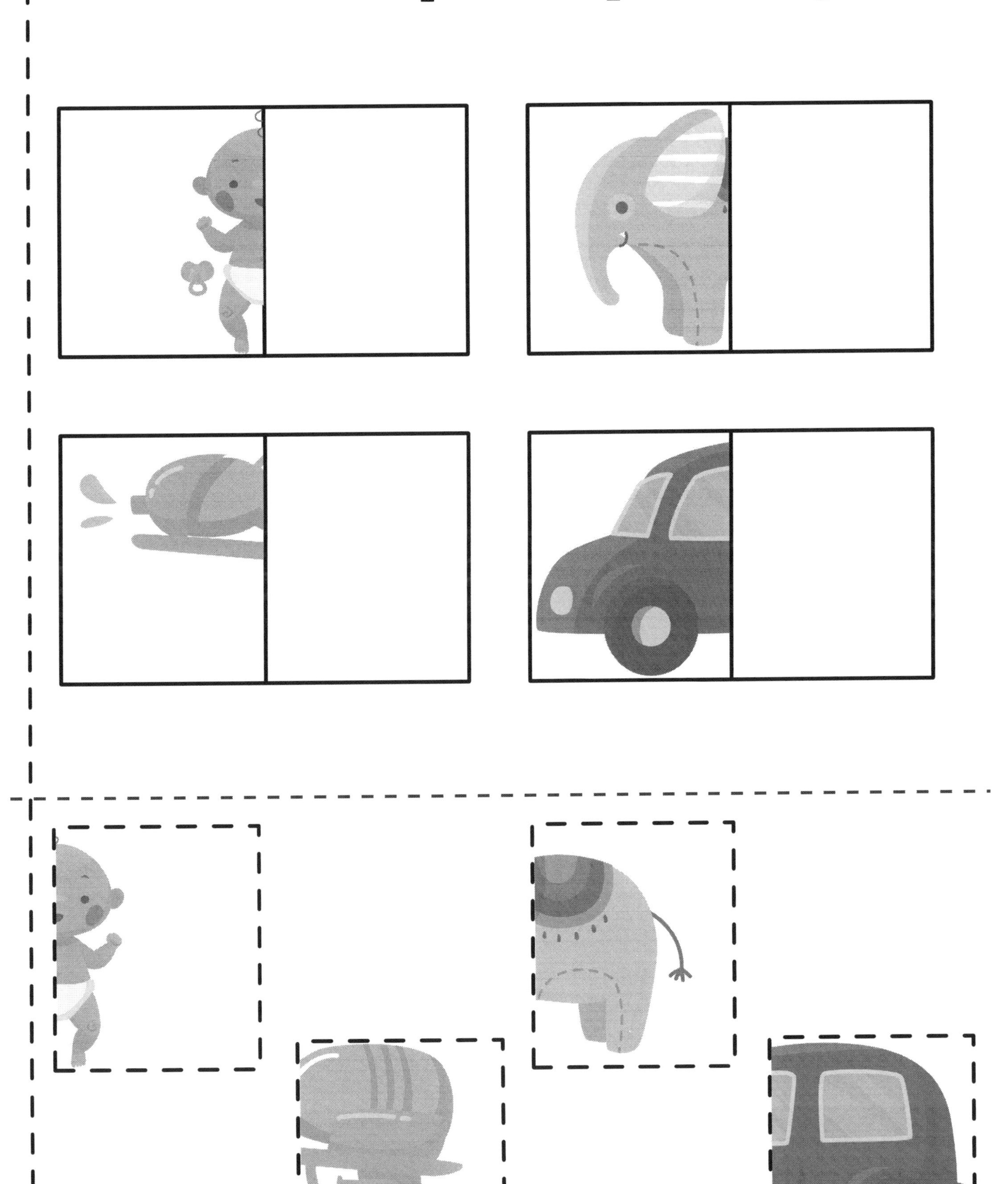

Find match and paste the pictures together

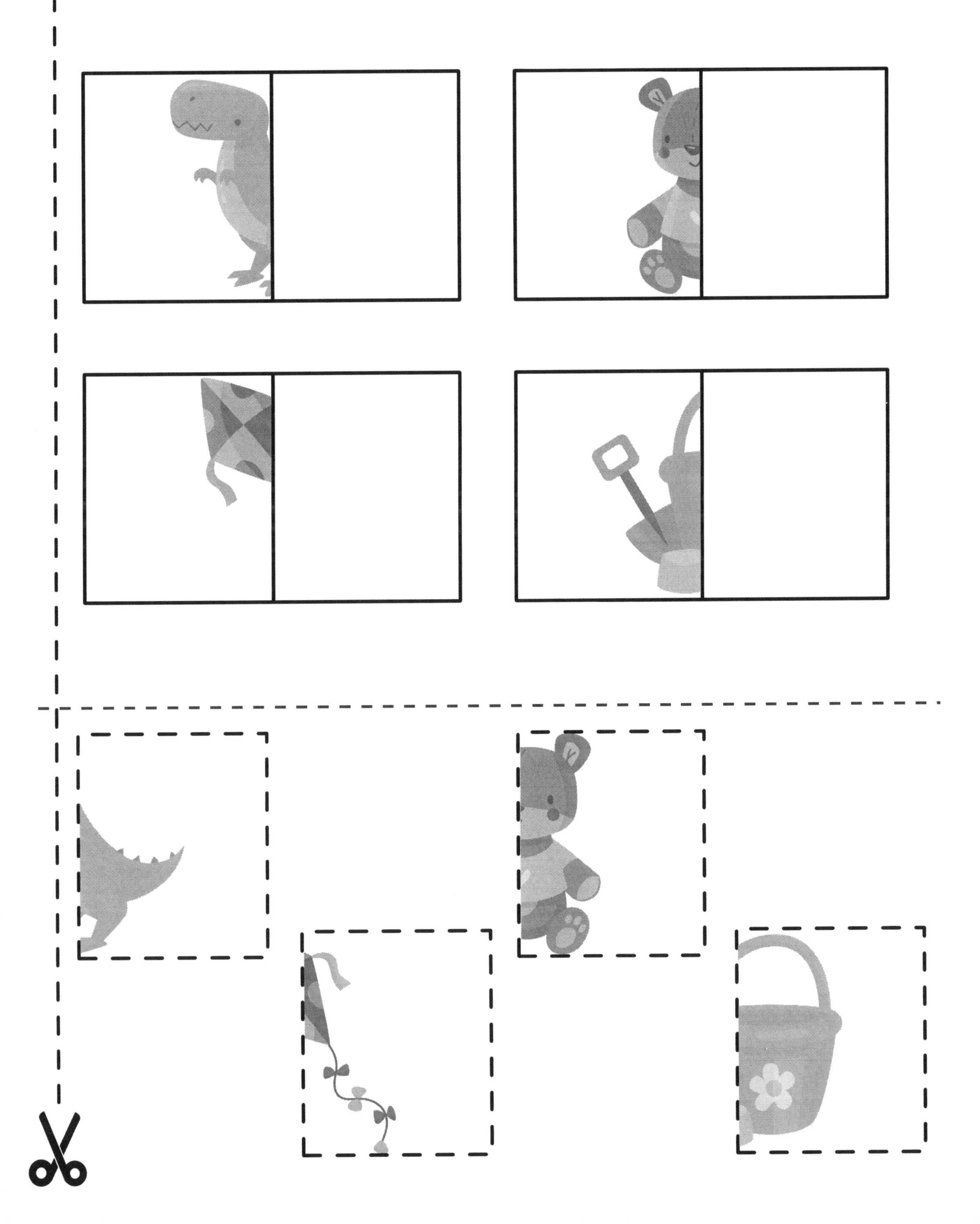

Find match and paste the pictures together

Cut the Puzzles and paste them on the next page

Paste here!

Cut the Puzzles and paste them on the next page

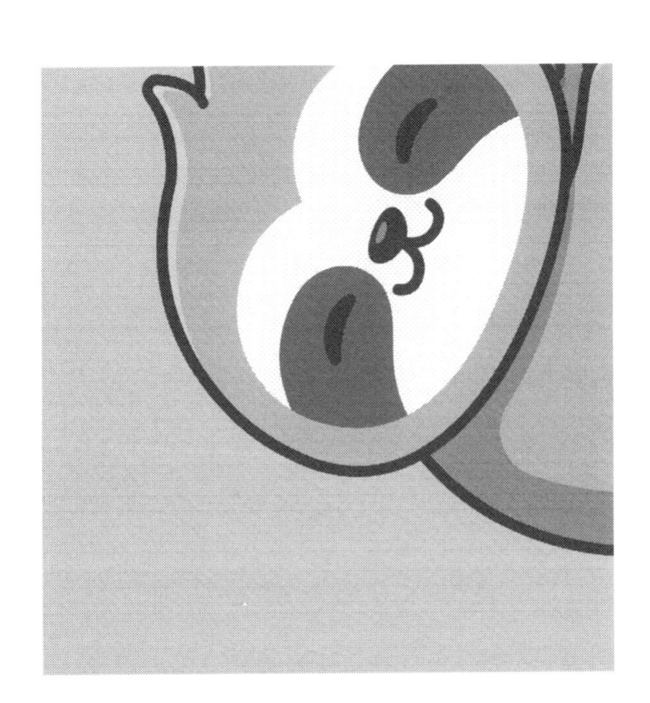

Paste here!

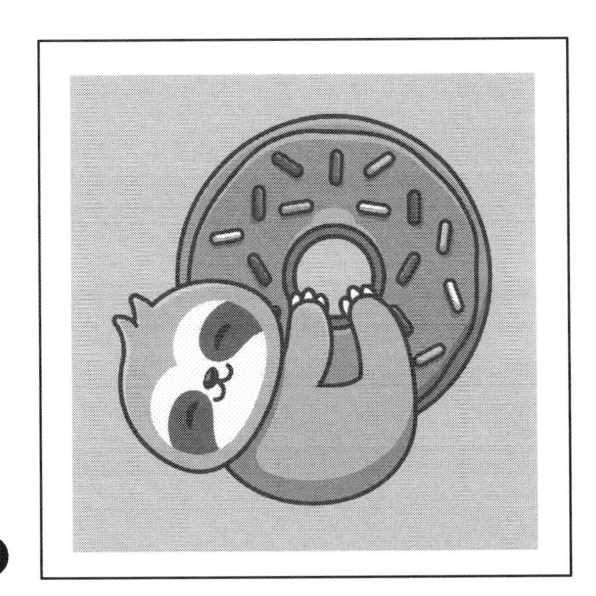

Cut the Puzzles and paste them on the next page

Paste here!

Cut the Puzzles and paste them on the next page

Paste here!

Cut the Puzzles and paste them on the next page

Paste here!

Cut and Glue

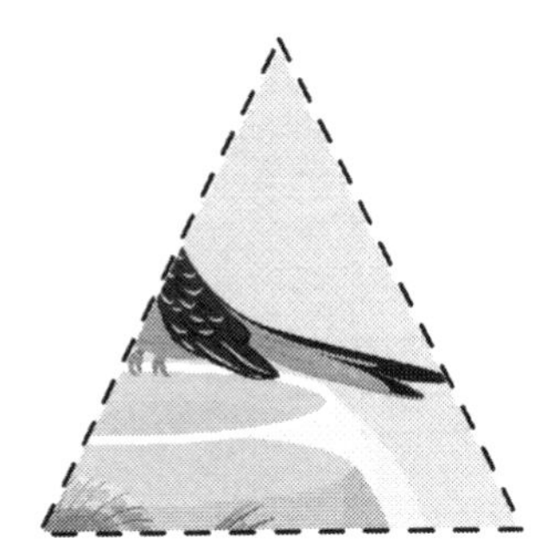

Cut and Glue

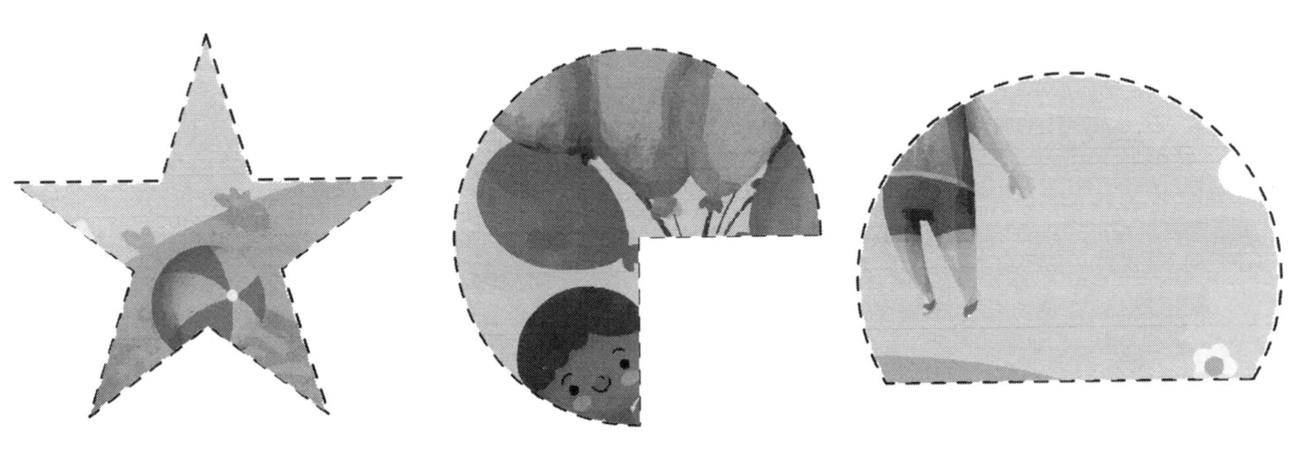

Cut and Glue

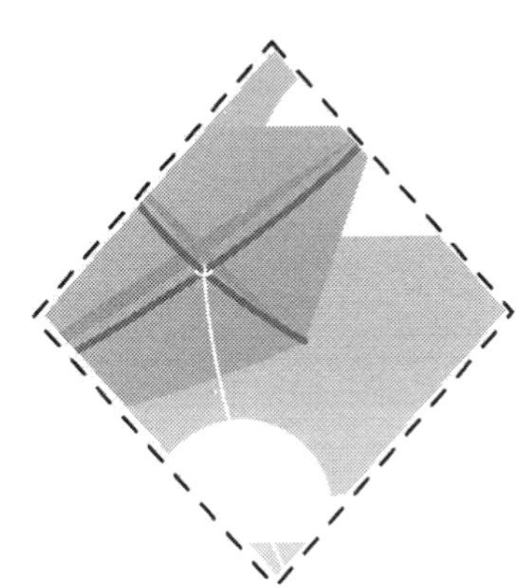

Cut and Glue

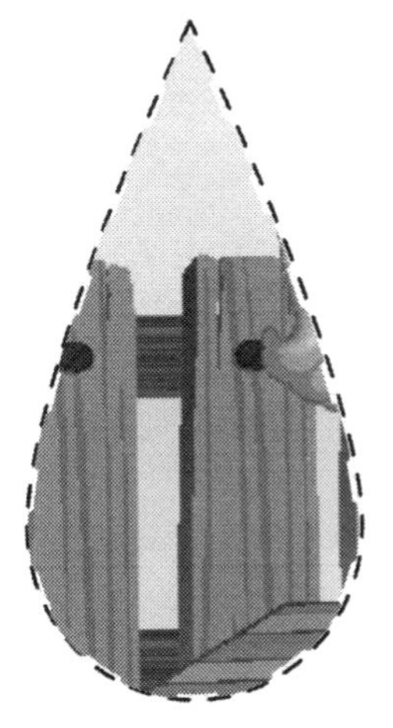

Cut and Glue

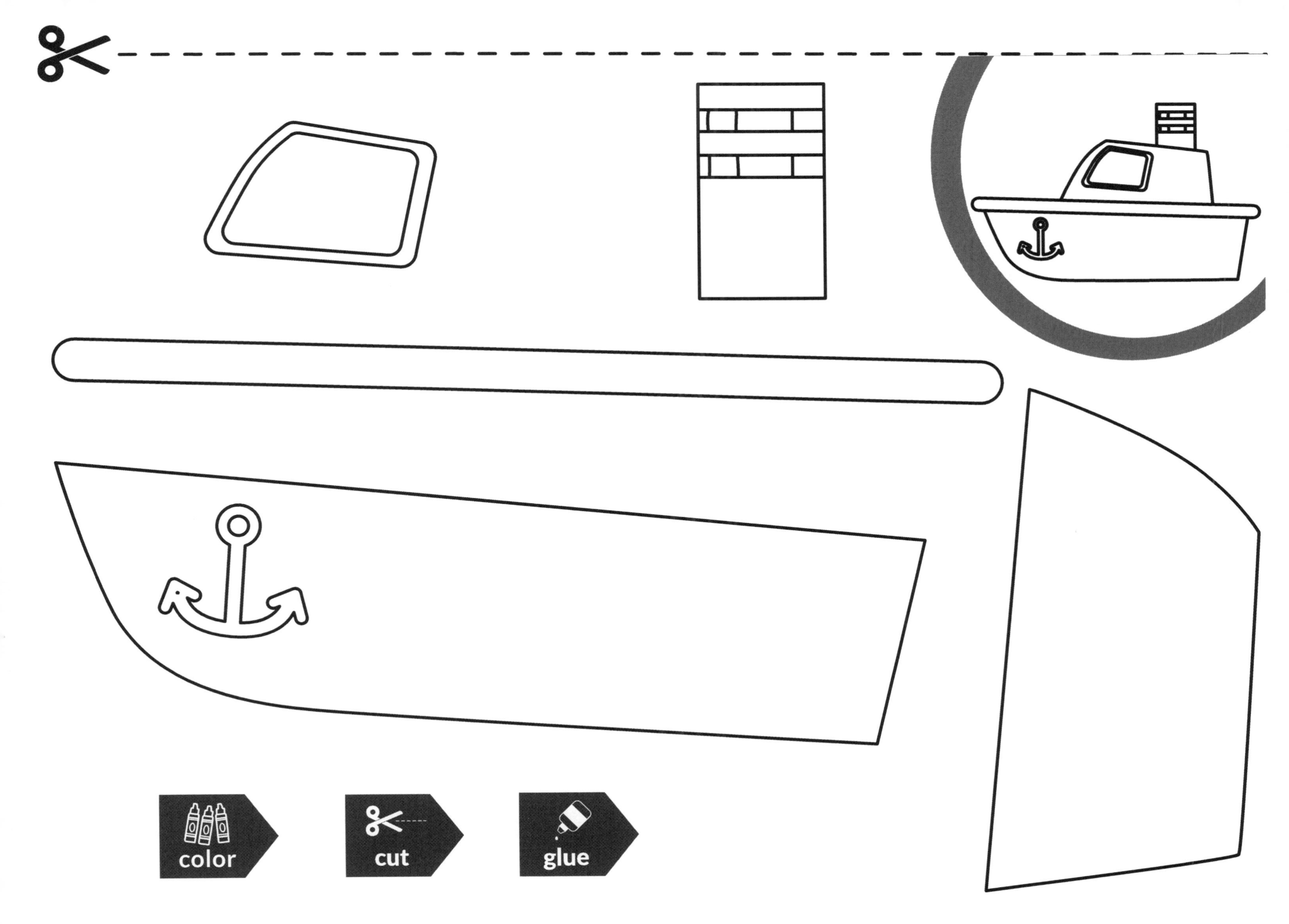
color
cut
glue

Paste here!

color
cut
glue

Paste here!

color
cut
glue

Paste here!

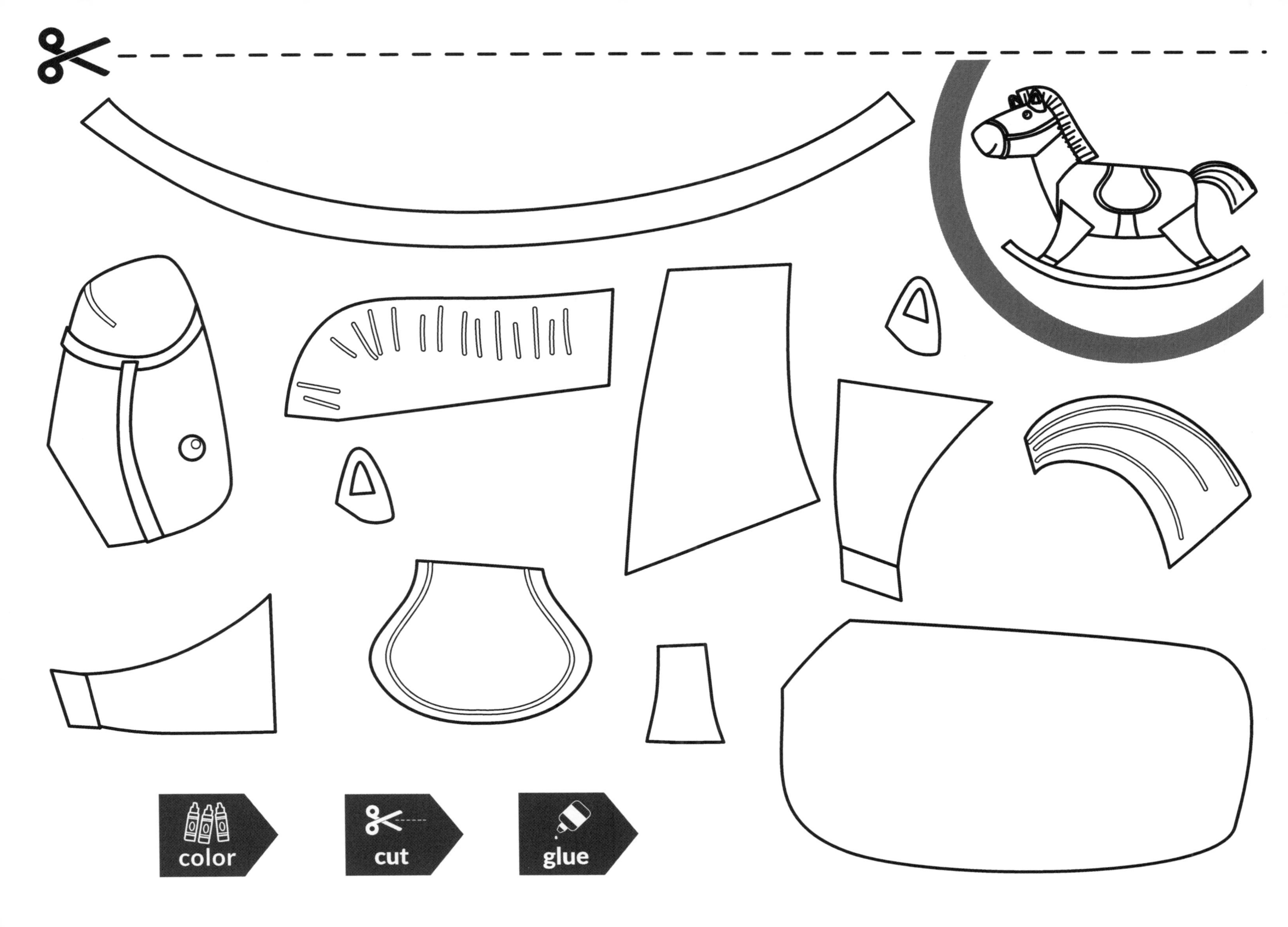
color
cut
glue

Paste here!

color
cut
glue

Paste here!

Cut and Glue

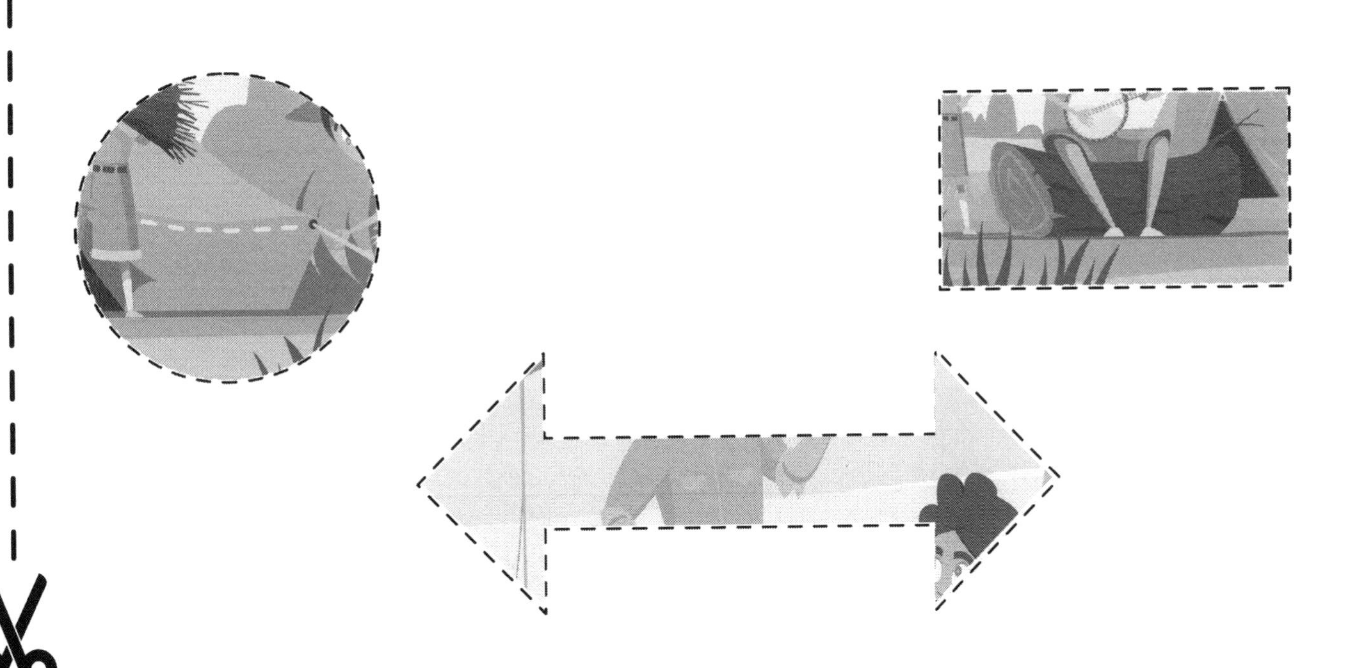

Cut and Glue

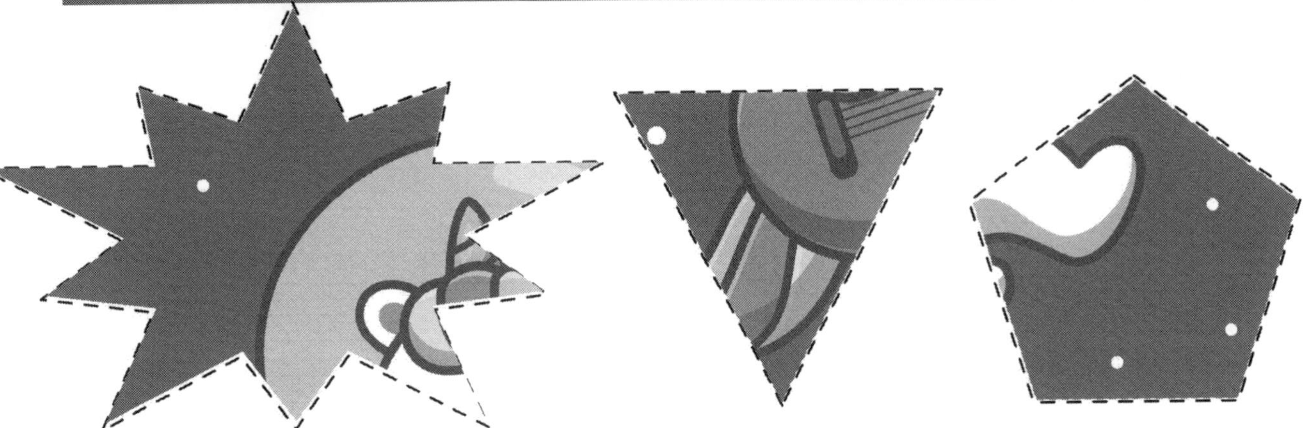

Cut and Glue

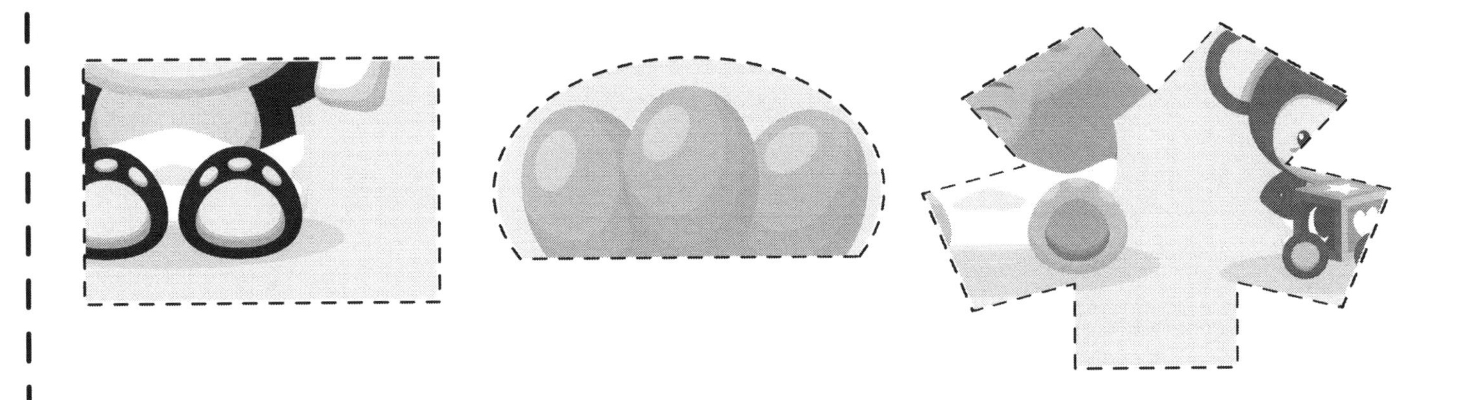

Cut and Glue

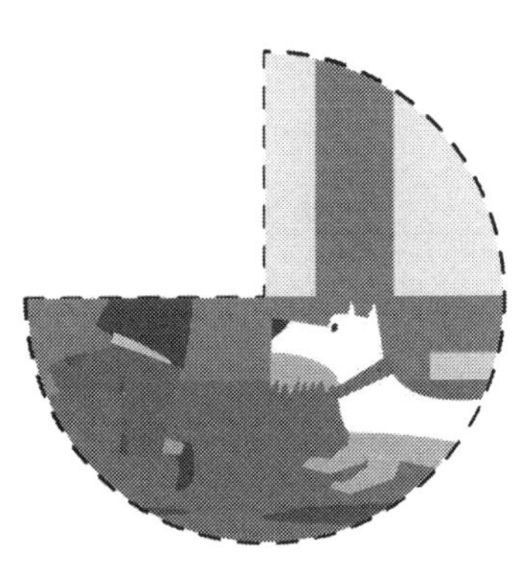

Cut and Glue

Thank you so much for purchasing "Cutting and Pasting" for kids!

We hope you had fun with the purchased book.

Please, leave your review and let others what you think about this book.
We will be forever grateful.

Thank you in advance.